We Have Fun

Karen J. Holinga, Ph.D.

Illustrated by Timberlee Harris

Published in Littleton, Colorado, by Happy Cheetah, LLC. Happy Cheetah and associated logos are trademarks owned by InquisiCorp Corporation.

Printed in the USA.

ISBN 978-1-935570-63-9

Your purchase
fuels efforts to end
illiteracy worldwide.

Table of Contents

The Park

We go to the park.

We take our backpacks and water.

We like to play
with the disc.

We like to eat
our sandwiches.
They are
delicious. Yum!

We like to climb
in the big trees.
Be careful!
Don't fall!

The Playground

We like to go to the playground.

We like to swing on the swings.

We like to slide
on the slides.

We like to climb on the monkey bars.

We like to ride on the merry-go-round. Giddy-up!

The Farm

We like to go
to the farm.

We can see
Meg the cow.

We like to see
Curly the pig.

We can see
Penny the hen.

Look at all the animals on the farm!

Staying at
Nana's and Papa's

Mom and Dad
want to go out.

We go to
Nana's and
Papa's house.

We make a hot campfire.

We eat yummy hot dogs.

We love
spending the
night at Nana's
and Papa's.
We have fun!

We Help

Nana's and Papa's house is fun.

We help bake
gingerbread
cookies.

We help plant
the flowers.

We help fix things.

Helping is fun!
Thank you, Nana
and Papa!

The Zoo

We like to visit

our zoo.

The gray elephant is very big.

The yellow and brown giraffe is very tall.

The hippo is very large.

The lion roars!
He can be very
scary!

The Beach

We like to go
to the beach.

We jump in
the cool waves.
Splash! Splash!
Splash!

We dig in the warm sand.
Dig! Dig! Dig!

We play with the beach ball in the hot sun.

We climb on the smooth rocks. It is fun to climb! We love the beach!

The Pet Shop

Let's go to the pet shop.

The birds are singing. Chirp! Chirp! Chirp!

The dogs are barking. Woof! Woof! Woof!

The fish are swimming. Swish! Swish! Swish!

The snakes are hissing. Hiss! Hiss! Hiss! Be careful!

The Fair

We went to our county fair.

We rode the horses on the merry-go-round. Giddy-up!

We slid on the red, blue, and yellow slides. Zoom! Zoom! Zoom!

We bumped in the blue, red, and yellow bumper cars. Bump! Bump! Bump!

We ate yummy food. It was delicious! I like pizza best!

The Aquarium

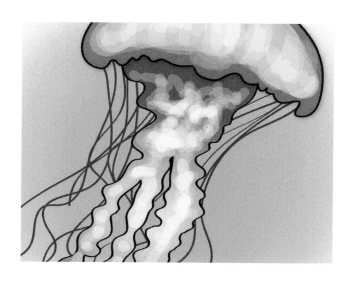

We went to the
aquarium.

We saw the sand eels playing in the sand.

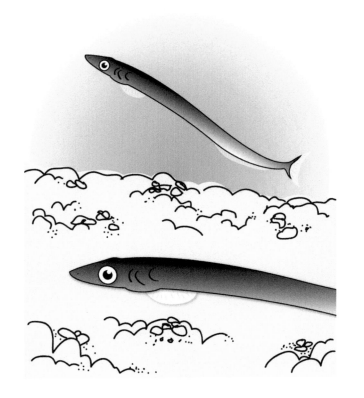

We saw the jellyfish floating in the water.

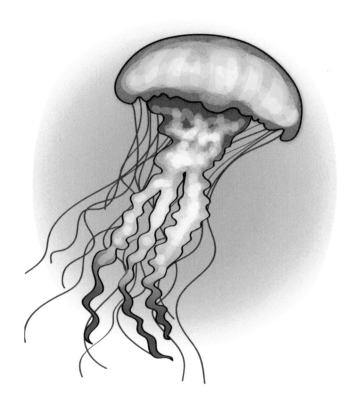

We watched the pretty sea horse.

We watched a scuba diver feed the fish.
Be careful, scuba diver!